Beautiful bedtime stories

with Jesus

Beautiful bedtime stories with Jesus: Published 2014
by The Incorporated Catholic Truth Society,
40-46 Harleyford Road, London SE11 5AY.
Tel: 020 7640 0042; Fax 020 7640 0046;
www.CTSbooks.org

Copyright © 2014 The Incorporated Catholic Truth Society
in this English language edition.
Translated from the French edition by
Glynn MacNiven-Johnston.

ISBN : 978-1-78469-018-2

CTS Code CH58

Translated from the original French language edition,
Belles histoires pour s'endormir avec Jésus,
written by Charlotte Grossetête and illustrated by
Sibylle Delacroix, Dominique Mertens and Eric Puybaret.

ISBN : 978-2-72891-711-2

Copyright © Mame, Paris, 2013.

Beautiful bedtime stories

with Jesus

Text by Charlotte Grossetête

Illustrated by Sibylle Delacroix,
Dominique Mertens
and Eric Puybaret

CTS Children's Books

Contents

Jesus is Born

It was a freezing cold night and everyone in Bethlehem had already been asleep for hours. The lights were out in all the houses. There was only one small chink of light showing through the plank walls of a stable. There, in the stable, a baby was lying in a manger. His mother, Mary, was looking at him lovingly. From time to time she tenderly murmured her child's name, 'Jesus'. Then Joseph nodded his head saying, 'God saves' because that's what the name Jesus means.

Joseph knew that Jesus wasn't actually his son, because Mary had been given this baby by God; but he also knew that God had given him his son to look after and he was happy to become Jesus's father on earth. As for Jesus, he was fast asleep. The lamp lit up his tiny face; nobody in Bethlehem knew it yet, but this face would become the light of the world.

In the hills nearby, another light was burning. It was a fire. Some shepherds who were spending the night with their flocks were lying in a circle around the embers to keep warm.

Suddenly an angel appeared to them. Waking with a start the shepherds threw themselves face down on the ground. Then the angel said to them, 'Don't be afraid. Tonight a saviour has been born to you. Hurry down to Bethlehem. You will find the child there, lying in a manger.'

The shepherds took their sheep and hurried to the town while a crowd of other angels began to sing in the heavens, 'Glory to God in the highest and peace on earth to the people that he loves.'

When the shepherds came noisily into the stable, Jesus smiled as if he felt at home with these poor people. Did this tiny little boy already know that he would one day be the shepherd of men?

The shepherds left to go back to the hills but Jesus and his parents weren't alone for long. A bright star had risen over the horizon, and some Magi from a far off country had been following it. They knew this star was guiding them to the King of the Universe and they were travelling as fast as possible, anxious to find the child.

When they finally arrived at the stable, they bowed down at Jesus's feet and placed three gifts in front of him: gold, frankincense and myrrh. Mary's face was suddenly serious as she looked from the presents to her child.

'Gold is the gift given to kings.' she said to herself, 'And frankincense is given to God alone, but myrrh is medicine for those who suffer. Is my son going to suffer one day?'

The Magi knelt in front of Jesus for a long time. When they were about to leave, they said to Joseph and Mary 'We have to go back through Jerusalem. King Herod is expecting us. He wants to know where your child is so that he can come and worship him too.' At those words, Mary shivered, but she didn't know why.

When night came, an angel appeared to the Magi and said to them, 'Don't go back to Herod. He lied to you. He wants to harm the child.' So the Magi went home by another way. Then the angel appeared to Joseph too 'Wake up quickly,' the angel told him. 'King Herod is jealous and he is sending soldiers to Bethlehem to kill the child. Run away to Egypt. You'll be safe there.'

Joseph got up as quickly as he could, put Mary and Jesus on a small donkey and set off in the direction of the desert as the sound of clanging weapons approached Bethlehem. The family stayed in Egypt for a few years. Then one day the angel appeared to Joseph again. 'Herod is dead,' said the angel. 'You can go home. The child won't be in danger anymore.'

Happy to be back in their own country, Joseph and Mary set up home in Nazareth where Joseph worked as a carpenter. They brought Jesus up there. Jesus grew in strength and wisdom. He learned to be a carpenter like Joseph, and helped his mother in the house. He prayed with his parents and played with the other boys in the village. Everyone loved him, but nobody knew who he really was.

Jesus was now twelve years old. Under his unruly hair, his face was still childlike, but he had grown and his hands were skilled in using carpentry tools. His hands were also very quick to help whenever a neighbour was in need. But these child's hands also knew how to stay lifted up in prayer, palms raised to heaven; but nobody in Nazareth knew about that, because when he wanted to speak to his Father, Jesus preferred to go up into the hills and pray in secret.

That spring, as he did every year, Joseph closed his workshop for a week. It was the feast of Passover and the Jews used to go up to Jerusalem to pray at the Temple. Jesus and his parents enjoyed making this pilgrimage together.

On the way, Joseph and Mary told Jesus stories about other journeys they had made with him; how they went to Bethlehem before he was born, and how they escaped to Egypt to get away from Herod.

Jesus already knew these stories, but he enjoyed listening to them and picturing them in his mind, because he didn't remember them himself. Then, leaving his parents to walk together he ran off to join his friends from Nazareth who were making the pilgrimage too. The journey passed quickly and Jesus shouted out in surprise when he saw the walls of Jerusalem on the horizon: 'Already?!' He left his group of friends to wait for Joseph and Mary 'See you here in a week' the boys called out to him. 'We'll journey back together!'

As Jesus entered the city with his parents, the streets began to fill up. Crowds of people from every country were making their way towards the Temple. But Jesus frowned as he entered the Temple courtyard. There were merchants there talking loudly and jingling their bags of money. 'They've no business here,' Jesus muttered. 'What did you say?' asked Mary. Jesus never normally got angry, and his parents looked at him astonished. But it was the time for prayer, so all three of them went to wash their hands and lose themselves in the joy of speaking to God.

At the end of the feast of Passover, Joseph and Mary met up again with their neighbours from Nazareth and they left Jerusalem together. 'Where's Jesus?' Mary asked, as they passed through the city gates. 'He must have caught up with his friends,' said Joseph. 'They wanted to travel back together.'

Joseph and Mary travelled for the whole day without worrying. That evening, they saw Jesus's friends running to catch up with them. 'Isn't Jesus with you?' they asked, out of breath. 'We waited for three hours by the side of the road. He's forgotten we were going to meet up.'

'Where has he got to?' cried Mary. 'We'll have to go back and look for him,' said Joseph, his face dark with worry.

Poor Mary! Poor Joseph! They went all the way back to Jerusalem and spent the whole night searching the deserted streets. The sun came up and dispelled the darkness, but Jesus still couldn't be found. Desperately worried, his parents spent three days looking everywhere in the city. Finally Joseph said, 'Let's go and pray. We need God to give us strength.'

When they entered the Temple, they heard a child's voice echoing from under the colonnades. Joseph and Mary thought they must be dreaming. They could hear Jesus speaking! They went further in. Their son was there, talking about God. He was surrounded by priests and learned men, listening to him and nodding their heads with respect. Despite their age and knowledge, they looked like pupils listening to a teacher. From time to time, they asked the boy questions. His answers were luminous and full of wisdom.

Mary was so relieved she started to scold Jesus 'My son, what a fright you've given us. We've spent three days looking for you!' Jesus gave Mary a look that said 'Sorry, Mum,' but he said, 'You should have known I would be in my Father's house.'

Mary and Joseph opened their eyes wide with surprise at his answer. Mary spent the whole journey back to Nazareth thinking about what had just happened. She remembered what an old man called Simeon had said to her when Jesus was a baby: 'On account of your son, a sword of pain will pierce your heart'. She had just suffered because of her son. One day she might suffer even more. She needed to be ready. Her son did not belong only to her.

The Call of the Disciples

Like a mirror, Lake Tiberias reflected the rose-coloured mists of dawn. Two boats were making for shore leaving lines of foam in their wake. In the first boat were Simon Peter and his brother Andrew; close behind, followed their friends James and John. Simon's eyes opened wide with surprise when he saw a huge crowd of people on the shore. Normally, the country round about was deserted, especially at that hour of the morning. 'What's going on?' muttered Simon. 'I've no idea,' Andrew mumbled sleepily.

The brothers were both tired and grumpy. They had been fishing all night and hadn't caught a single fish. They reckoned they would have been better off staying at home and sleeping.

At that moment the sun rose from behind a hill, and its rays shone on the huge crowd. Andrew squinted. 'There's a man in white in the middle of those people', he said. 'He seems to be talking to them. They're all here because of him.'

As the boat reached the shore, Simon shrugged and said, 'We've no time to go see what's going on. We have to wash the nets.' The fishermen got out of their boat and began to clean their nets. Bent over their work, they were too caught up to notice the crowd coming towards them. Suddenly, a shadow made them look up. The man in white was standing in front of them. People were crowding round and calling out from all sides, 'Jesus, Master, speak to us again!' 'Tell us who your Father is.' 'Explain the Kingdom of God to us!'

To the brothers' great surprise, Jesus got into their boat. He said to them, 'Come on, get in! Put out a bit from the shore.' Simon and Andrew did as they were told and stopped the boat not far from the lakeside. Jesus stood up in front of the mast and again began to speak to the sea of faces. This way, everyone could hear better.

Sitting open-mouthed in the boat, Simon and Andrew listened to Jesus too, and even though they were tired they felt as if there was a great light shining in their hearts. They felt as if they were really close to God, this Father Jesus was speaking about.

The sun was already high in the sky when Jesus stopped speaking. Reluctantly, the people started to leave. Then Jesus said to Simon and Andrew, 'Put out into the lake and let down your nets.' The two fishermen sighed. Those words brought back bad memories. 'We've worked all night and caught nothing,' they said.' But, since it's you that's asking, we'll go back and try again.'

Peter signalled to James and John to follow them, and the two boats made for the middle of the lake. Once there fishermen threw their nets into the dark water. Almost at once they felt the nets pulling. 'How many fish are there down there?' gasped Simon. 'Watch out!' shouted Andrew. 'The net this side is so full it's going to tear.'

The two fishermen tried hard to haul in their catch, but they couldn't, so they called over to James and John to come and help them. Jesus watched the four men working together, smiling quietly. When they finally managed to pull the catch into the boat they were dumbfounded by how many and how many different kinds of fish they could see through the torn net. Shaking, Simon threw himself at Jesus's feet. 'Go away from me, Master,' he exclaimed. 'I am a sinful man.' His companions nodded in agreement. They too felt very small in front of Jesus. But he said to them, 'Follow me. You used to be fishers of fish; but with me, you'll be fishers of men. You will catch crowds of people and lead them to life.'

The two boats were so heavy with fish that it took them some time to get to land. Once they were there, the fishermen jumped ashore without even thinking about taking their nets. They followed Jesus who had already set out again to make God known to yet more people.

These fishermen became the first disciples; soon, they were joined by eight others. By living with Jesus, these twelve men came to have the word of God written in their hearts so they, in their turn, could make God known to all the world.

Jesus Heals

'Jesus has come back! He's at Simon Peter's house!'. In seconds, the peaceful village of Capernaum erupted. People came out of every door, fishermen abandoned the lakeshore, shepherds hurtled down the hillside, everyone rushed to Simon Peter's house. Jesus really was there. 'Rabbi', said the first breathless arrivals. 'Why did you leave the village? We thought you were going to stay here forever.'

'I was in Galilee,' said Jesus. 'In Nazareth, where you grew up?' 'No. I walked from town to town announcing the Kingdom of God. My Father's word can't be shut up in just one village. It has to spread out so that everyone can hear it.' The crowd tried to cram into the room, but the house was too small for everyone to get in. Entire families had to stay outside squashed up against the door to hear what Jesus was saying.

A voice called out from the crowd: 'They say you've healed a lot of people recently, Rabbi. Even lepers.' There was murmuring then, both admiring and unbelieving. How could anyone cure this incurable illness? Jesus said nothing in reply, and in the silence that followed, a commotion was heard outside. 'Sorry! Mind your backs!' said one voice. 'Can't you see we're carrying a stretcher?' said another. 'Our friend is paralysed and wants to see the rabbi.'

'We're so packed in we can't breathe,' said the villagers. 'How do you think you can get through?' Jesus was listening to this, but he made no comment. He began to speak about God. A few moments later there was a noise from the ceiling. Everyone looked up just in time to see the roof open in a cloud of dust. The paralysed man's four friends had climbed up and made a big hole. From there they gently lowered the stretcher into the room on ropes.

Some people started to get annoyed. Others smiled, though, touched by the boldness of these men who were ready to do anything to help their friend. Jesus smiled as well. The stretcher landed just in front of him. Jesus looked at the man lying there and said, 'My son, your sins are forgiven'.

In the room, there were some scribes who reckoned they knew everything about God. They were shocked and thought 'Who does this rabbi think he is? Only God can forgive sins.' Jesus knew what was in their hearts. He said to them, 'What is easier? To say to a paralysed man "Your sins are forgiven" or to say, "Get up. Pick up your stretcher and walk"? Well then, to show you the Son of Man has the power to forgive sins, I say to you "Get up. Pick up your stretcher and go home".'

He had scarcely spoken before the paralysed man stood up, on legs which had never walked, and took up the stretcher in his skinny arms with a strength which amazed the crowd. People said to each other, 'I've never seen anything like it!' while the man went on his way happy.

There were miracles wherever Jesus went. Another day, while he was passing through Jericho, surrounded as always by a vast crowd, there was a cry from far off. 'Jesus, Son of David, Have mercy on me!' Jesus's disciples were astonished. 'Who is this man?' 'Oh, it's only blind Bartimaeus,' they were told. 'He spends his days begging at the side of the road.' 'Jesus, Son of David, have mercy on me!' This time, Bartimaeus shouted loud enough to be heard above the noise of the crowd. 'Be quiet! You're deafening us!' the people near him protested. But Jesus stopped. 'Call him over,' he said. The message was passed from person to person, until the people near him said to Bartimaeus. 'Take courage. Get up! He's calling you.' The blind man threw his cloak to the ground and bounded towards Jesus. 'What do you want me to do for you?' Jesus asked him. 'Rabbuni. Make me see.' Jesus smiled. When he had called Bartimaeus the blind man could have answered 'Jesus, you come over to me, because you can see and I can't,' but instead he had run over as quickly as possible with complete confidence. 'Go! Your faith has saved you,' said Jesus. Then, at once, Bartimaeus's eyes were filled with daylight. He could see! Like the rest of the crowd, he set out to follow Jesus, full of joy.

From Death to Life

Two men were walking along with bowed heads. The journey from Jerusalem to Emmaus had never seemed so long and difficult before. Their feet felt heavy and their sandals kept catching on sharp stones. 'The Rabbi should never have died,' said the first man suddenly. 'Why did they hate him so much?' The two men sighed. Terrible scenes replayed in their minds. Jesus beaten by the soldiers; Jesus falling under the cross they made him carry; Jesus nailed to the wood; Jesus forgiving his enemies before he died. 'It's so unfair!' they both said at the same time. They heard footsteps behind them. They supposed it was a traveller who had caught up with them on the way. Being so discouraged, they were not going very fast.

'What are you talking about?' asked the stranger. They were amazed at his question. They glanced at him. 'You must be the only person who doesn't know what's happened,' said one. 'Don't you know Jesus of Nazareth was crucified on Friday? We thought he was the one who would free Israel and now all our hope is destroyed.'

His companion added, 'Some of his friends went to the graveyard this morning. They said the tomb was empty and Jesus has risen from the dead.' The first man shrugged. 'Come on, Cleopas, you know those women were imagining it.'

The stranger said to them, 'Your hearts are so slow to believe. Didn't you understand that the Messiah was to suffer before he entered into glory?' Still walking, he began to explain the scriptures to the two disciples. From the very beginning, he said, the scriptures have announced the coming of Jesus and spoken about his Passion and his Resurrection; so how could they be surprised at what had happened?

The travellers listened to him and, without knowing why, their spirits began to lift. They started to walk more quickly and arrived in Emmaus before they knew it. 'This is where we go our different ways,' said the stranger. 'Oh no!' the men begged him, 'Stay and eat with us. It'll be dark soon.'

When they were at table, the stranger took the bread, he blessed it and broke it to share it. This simple gesture reminded the two men of what the disciples had told them about the last meal Jesus shared with them. At once their eyes were opened, and they knew who it was in front of them: it was Jesus! They leapt up and would have bowed down before him; but he had disappeared.

'Why didn't we recognise him earlier?' Cleopas exclaimed. 'Our hearts burned within us when he spoke to us!' 'Let's go back to Jerusalem,' his companion said. 'We have to tell the others about this.'

Even though it was dark, the two men ran so fast that it only took them an hour to get back to the city. They rushed to where the disciples were. 'Jesus is truly risen!' shouted Cleopas, all out of breath. 'So you've seen him too?' exclaimed the disciples. 'He appeared today to Peter'. The friends hugged each other. Their sorrow had changed to joy, their mourning to rejoicing. For forty days, Jesus continued to appear to his disciples to show them that he really was alive.

Then he said to them: 'Now I'm going back to my Father, and you won't see me any more. But I'll send you the strength you need. You'll go out to all the countries of the world to baptise people in the name of the Father and of the Son and of the Holy Spirit; and I'll be with you always, to the end of time.' After he had said that, he rose into the sky and disappeared.

Left alone the disciples spent ten strange, sad days. It seemed to them they had lost Jesus for a second time. They didn't talk about him in public in case they were arrested.

The day of Pentecost came round. It was a great feast for all the Jews, but Jesus's friends didn't share the joy that was everywhere in Jerusalem. They stayed at home. Suddenly a gust of wind filled their house and tongues of fire came down and rested on their heads. It was the Holy Spirit Jesus had promised. The disciples felt full of new courage. Now they would be able to announce the Good News to the whole world, without fear and with a joy that would never end.